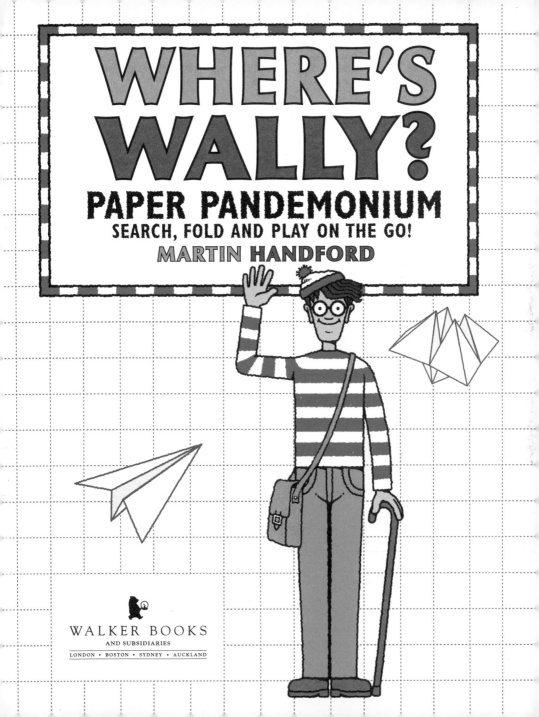

WHERE'S WALLY?

PAPER PANDEMONIUM

SEARCH, FOLD AND PLAY ON THE GO!

MARTIN HANDFORD

WALKER BOOKS
AND SUBSIDIARIES

LONDON · BOSTON · SYDNEY · AUCKLAND

HELLO, WALLY-WATCHERS!

I HOPE YOU'RE FEELING CRAFTY! HAVE YOU EVER WANTED TO RACE PAPER AEROPLANES? MAKE YOUR OWN FORTUNE TELLER? CREATE A FINGER PUPPET FRIEND? NOW'S YOUR CHANCE! BETWEEN THE PAGES OF THIS BOOK ARE ALL SORTS OF AMAZING 3D CRAFTS THAT ARE FANTASTICALLY FUN AND EASY TO MAKE.

JUST FOLLOW THE INSTRUCTIONS AND
START TEARING, TWISTING AND FOLDING
... LET THE PAPER PANDEMONIUM BEGIN!

ONE MORE THING! I'VE THROWN FIVE
RED-AND-WHITE PAPER AEROPLANES AND SENT
THEM FLYING ACROSS THE PAGES FOR YOU TO
FIND. LOOK OUT FOR ME IN EVERY SCENE, TOO!

GOOD LUCK!

Wally

FLIGHT SCHOOL

Before you make your own fleet of aeroplanes, it's time to brush up on the lingo! Search for all these technical terms that pilots need to know.

AVIATION   TURBULENCE   WINGS

NAVIGATION   MAYDAY   PASSENGER

P	A	G	N	O	W	M	N	T
R	R	E	A	A	I	R	K	U
E	O	Y	V	A	N	Y	D	R
G	F	T	I	A	G	A	D	B
N	A	V	G	R	S	I	O	U
E	T	Y	A	D	Y	A	M	L
S	T	R	T	Z	M	B	L	E
S	A	V	I	A	T	I	O	N
A	Q	V	O	A	T	I	O	C
P	O	F	N	R	B	I	J	E

BAGGAGE CLAIM

This unhappy passenger has lost their luggage!
Follow the clues to pick out the missing bag.

1. *I last saw it next to a brown suitcase*
2. *It's got two clasps and a handle*
3. *It's the same colour as Wally's trousers*

MORE THINGS TO FIND

- A tired cow
- A shovel
- A bat
- Hair in a bun
- The German flag

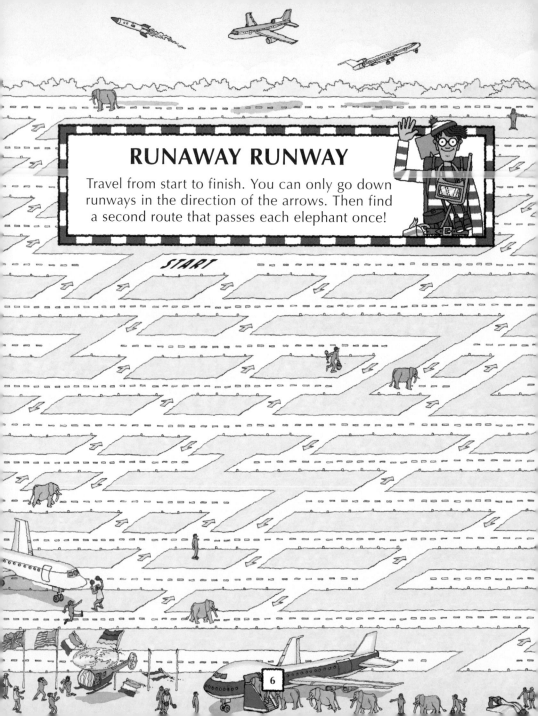

RUNAWAY RUNWAY

Travel from start to finish. You can only go down runways in the direction of the arrows. Then find a second route that passes each elephant once!

START

FINISH

MORE THINGS TO FIND

- [ ] A rocket
- [ ] A wind-sock
- [ ] A flying ace
- [ ] An open suitcase
- [ ] A French flag
- [ ] Three buckets

7

DESTINATION EVERYWHERE

Unscramble the letters in the "Destination" column to spell the names of twelve cities. Then search for flights with "WAL" in them to find out which places I'll be travelling to. Wow!

Depart	Destination	Flight	Arrive	Delays
10:00	WEN OYKR	WAL1	22:00	ON TIME
08:00	NOONLD	WDA1	07:00	ON TIME
22:00	GNHO NKGO	WOF1	10:30	1 HOUR
11:30	RASIP	WOF2	21:00	ON TIME
23:00	BUDAI	ODW2	06:00	ON TIME
22:00	AOS AULOP	WAL2	10:00	ON TIME
13:00	STERAMDAM	WZD1	21:00	1 HOUR
21:00	OTONTOR	WZD2	23:00	ON TIME
23:00	KYOTO	WAL4	13:00	ON TIME
10:00	REOM	WAL3	23:00	ON TIME
19:00	SOLO	ODW1	22:00	3 HOURS
07:00	DNEYYS	WDA2	09:00	ON TIME

MORE THINGS TO DO

* Did Wally catch all four flights? Starting with "WAL1", check the arrival time matches the departure time of "WAL2" and so on.

* Can you also find Wenda's, Woof's, Wizard Whitebeard's and Odlaw's abbreviated names?

* Can you work out where they flew to and if they caught their flights too?

WHERE TO?

Passengers boarding! But where are they heading?
Match the holiday-maker to their dream destination.

CUSTARDY COLIN
I love a holiday with a
detailed itinerary ... pie
throwing, horn honking,
juggling competition –
all the classics!

SILKY SADINE
I want to sea the sights
and let the stresses of
everyday life wash away
somewhere turtley
fintastic.

MUSTANG MEG
Anywhere wild and free
is good for me, as long
as there's gold to steal.
Yeehaw!

SLIDING SOLOMON
I'm pining for somewhere
I can just chill and get
some piste and
quiet.

BIRDS OF A FEATHER

Everything here is on the move! Match the pairs (or more) of flying creatures, characters and aircraft to reveal the odd one out.

MORE THINGS TO DO

Tell these jokes to a friend to get them giggling:

* Where do royal birds live? *Duckingham Palace!*

* What do you get when you cross Wizard Whitebeard with an aeroplane? *A flying sorcerer!*

* Can I tell you some jokes about paper aeroplanes? *Never mind, they're tearable!*

FLIP-FLOP FLIGHTS

Sit opposite a friend so you both have a flight destination facing you. Who can find the holiday-maker silhouettes in their scene first?

A
B
C
D
E
F
G

FLIP-FLOP FLIGHTS

Sit opposite a friend so you both have a flight destination facing you. Who can find the holiday-maker silhouettes in their scene first?

A
B
C
D
E
F
G

PILOT PASS

Before you take off, you'll need a pilot's licence. Fill in the box below and stick in or draw your own photo! You can use your real identity or create a flying persona.

PILOT PASS

Name: ....

Aircraft: ....

....

Special Skills:

....

....

....

Destination:

....

PILOT PASS

Name: **Captain Woof, AKA "Lead Foot"**

Aircraft: **Helicopter**

Special Skills:

Fetching

passengers

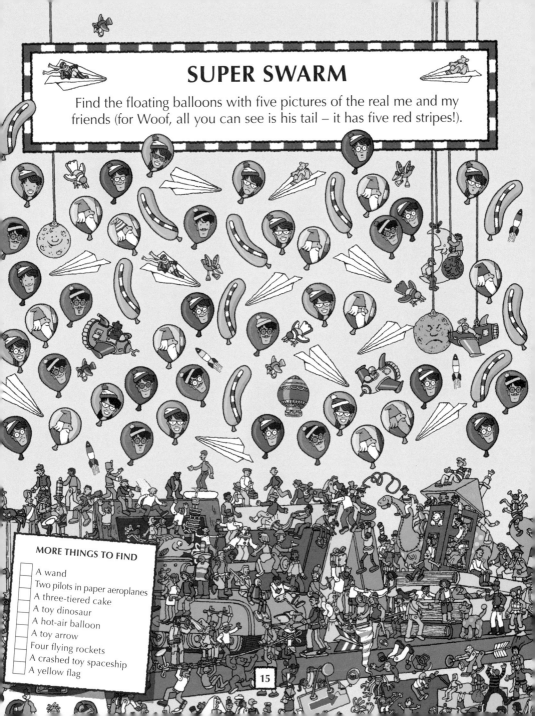

SUPER SWARM

Find the floating balloons with five pictures of the real me and my friends (for Woof, all you can see is his tail – it has five red stripes!).

MORE THINGS TO FIND

- A wand
- Two pilots in paper aeroplanes
- A three-tiered cake
- A toy dinosaur
- A hot-air balloon
- A toy arrow
- Four flying rockets
- A crashed toy spaceship
- A yellow flag

15

PLANE EASY

All right, folks, we're cleared for take-off.
Follow the instructions below to make
your very own fleet of aeroplanes!

① Check you are starting on the correct side of the paper, then fold it in half vertically.

② Fold the top corner down to meet the opposite edge.

③ Repeat the fold in **step 2** with the new flap.

④ Fold it over one more time.

⑤ Turn the paper over …

⑥ … and repeat **steps 2-4** on the other side.

⑦ Time to fly your plane!

TAKE-OFF TRICKS

Try adding one of these materials to the tip of your aeroplane for a smoother flight path!

* A paperclip
* Tape
* A dab of glue

COCKPIT COMPETITION

Find a friend and take on some fierce flying feats:

* Who can fly their plane the furthest?
* Which plane can fly the fastest?
* Chose a (safe!) target, and see who can hit it first!
* Throw your plane back and forth with a friend and see how many times in a row you can catch it.

Start folding with this side
of the paper upwards.
The plane title
should be in the
top right-hand
corner.

Instructions on page 16

Start folding with this side of the paper upwards. The plane title should be in the top right-hand corner.

OD-HAWK D91

Instructions on page 16

Start folding with this side of the paper upwards. The plane title should be in the top right-hand corner.

CLOWN AIR

Instructions on page 16

Start folding with this side
of the paper upwards.
The plane title
should be in the
top right-hand
corner.

Name and
create your
own plane!

Instructions on page 16

Instructions on page 33

Start folding with this side of the paper upwards. The spaceship title should be on the side of the paper facing away from you.

DRAGON-FLYER V233

Instructions on page 33

Start folding with this side of the paper upwards. The spaceship title should be on the side of the paper facing away from you.

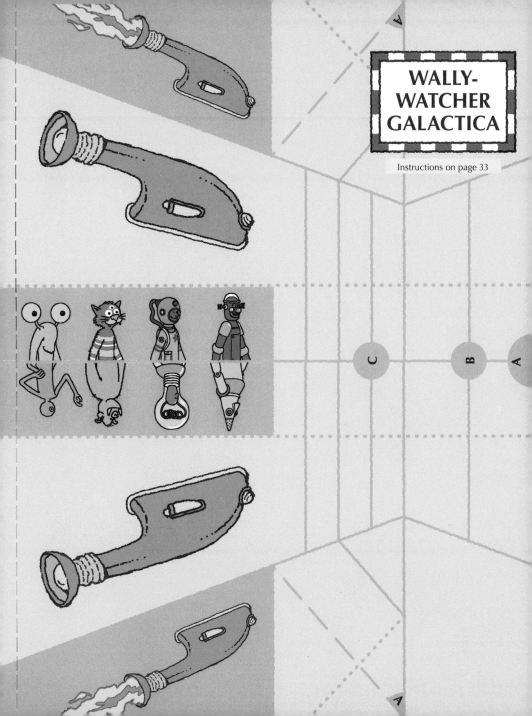

WALLY-
WATCHER
GALACTICA

Instructions on page 33

Start folding with this side of the paper upwards. The spaceship title should be on the side of the paper facing away from you.

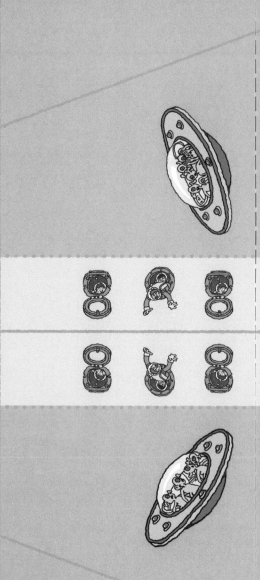

Name and create your own spaceship!

Instructions on page 33

A

C

B

A

A

Start folding with this side of the paper upwards. The spaceship title should be on the side of the paper facing away from you.

PERMISSION TO LAUNCH

Now you've conquered the skies, it's time to launch into the stratosphere! Follow these instructions to paper craft your way to the stars at light speed!

① Place the paper horizontally with the plane title face down in the top right corner. Fold it into quarters, then open it out again.

② Fold the top of the paper down to meet the middle crease. This will create a flap.

③ Fold in the top corners so that they meet the bottom of the flap and the middle crease. All three "A"s on the template will meet when you do this.

④ Fold the top down along line "B" to the dashed line, making a new flap.

⑤ Double the new flap by folding it in half along line "C" to meet the dashed line again.

⑥ Turn the paper over then fold it in half from left to right.

⑦ Fold back both wings along the dotted line on your template (shown here).

⑧ Your spaceship is ready to launch!

SHOOT FOR THE STARS

* Time how long you can keep your spaceship flying!

* Take your spaceship outside. Throw it first into the wind, then against it. Where does it land and how does it fly?

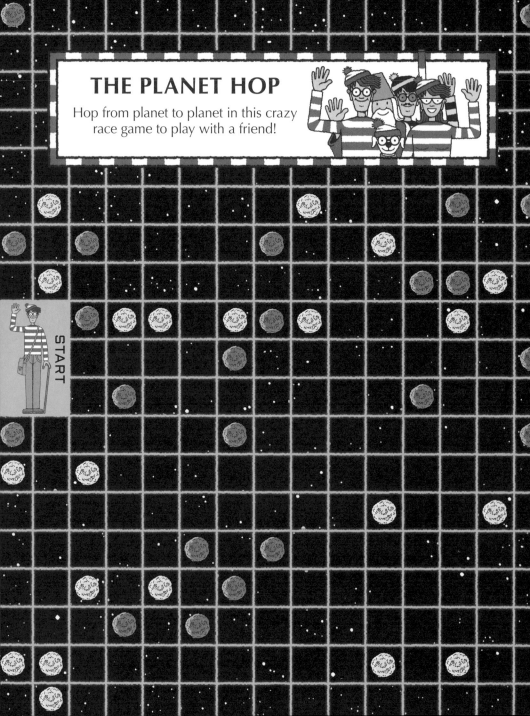

THE PLANET HOP

Hop from planet to planet in this crazy race game to play with a friend!

START

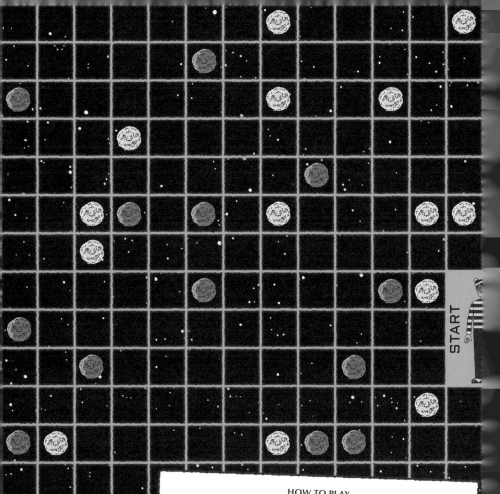

START

HOW TO PLAY

✱ Use your finger to follow each move. No need to use a counter!

✱ One player starts on Wally, and moves from red planet to red planet, one planet at a time.

✱ The other player starts on Odlaw, and moves from yellow planet to yellow planet, one planet at a time.

✱ At each turn, move in a straight line (up, down, left and right).

✱ If your path is blocked, retrace your steps and find a new route!

✱ The winner is the first player to get to a planet next to their opponent's starting square.

TIME AND SPACE MAZE

Find the yellow rocket a route out of the maze, picking up four crew members on the way. You can't pass clocks that have struck midnight! Tick, tock!

MORE THINGS TO FIND

Search the grey clocks for:

- Three clocks with their numbers in the wrong order
- A clock that says 5 o'clock
- A clock with a number missing

36

PLANETS ALIGNING

The sun is at the centre of our solar system but it seems to be missing its planets! Fit them all into the grid below.

MERCURY

JUPITER

VENUS

URANUS

S
U
N

NEPTUNE

EARTH

MARS

SATURN

STAR-GAZE DAZE

Pair up any stars with pictures that seem similar and then spot the three differences between each pair. It's extra eye-boggling!

MORE THINGS TO DO

* Wizard Whitebeard loves space music. Can you find nine stars in the shape of notes?

38

WANDERING LINES

Blue martians like to sleepwalk! How many rows of the same three do you see? A row can only be straight or diagonal, and Wizard Whitebeard's found one for you!

CONSTELLATION CONUNDRUM

While looking through my trusty telescope I discovered a new constellation! Join the stars together to see what shape it makes.

40

MORE THINGS TO DO

* Find the real version of the constellation you've drawn somewhere else in this scene!

WRITTEN IN THE STARS

Cross out the stars to find a message about your destiny. Double stars = a space!

```
T * H * E * R * E * * I * S *
* M * A * G * I * C * W * I
* T * H * I * N * * Y * O * U
! * * S * A * Y * * T * H *
I * S * * S * T * A * R * R *
Y * * S * P * E * L * L : *
* G * R * E * A * T * * S * T
* A * R * R * Y * * P * O * W
* E * R , * * I * S * U *
M * M * O * N * * T * H * E
* E * . * * W * I * T * H *
* A * N * * A * B * R * A *
C * A * D * A * B * R * A *
* O * N * E , * * T * W *
O * , * * T * H * R * E * E *!
```

CRYSTAL CLEAR

Stare deep into the magical crystal ball …
what do you see? Draw it in the space below!

SPELL-DUKO

My pantry of potions needs reordering! To avoid magical mayhem, colour in the white bottles. Each different coloured potion must appear once in each nine-square shelf but never in the same row or column.

SEA-PERSTITION

Adventuring pirates have stumbled upon all sorts of enchanted treasures! Can you spot these swashbuckling sights in this scene?

MORE THINGS TO FIND

- [ ] A rubber duck
- [ ] A quill
- [ ] Four ruby medallions
- [ ] A dizzy pirate
- [ ] A blue blanket
- [ ] Five eyepatches
- [ ] Shards of pottery
- [ ] Eight pirates with their tongues out

SPELL-TACULAR!

These four words have stretched out in a spectacular star shape.
Can you train your eyes to read them?

START HERE!

Clue: hold the book in front of your nose and tilt it backwards. Read the word in front of you, then turn the book to the right and read the next word and so on.

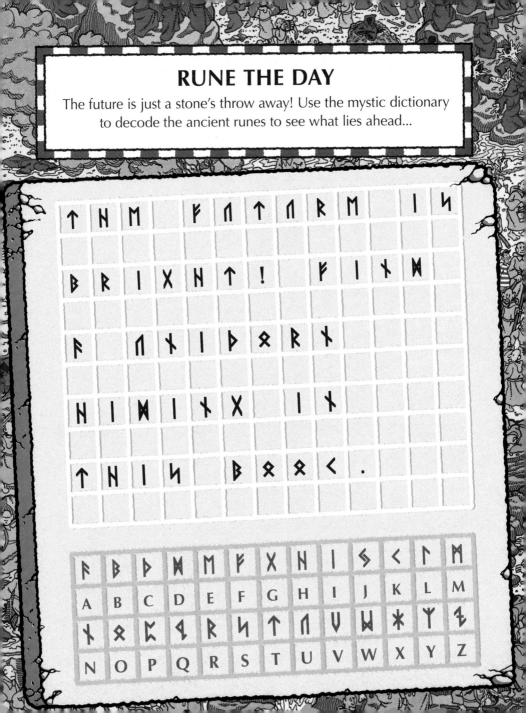

RUNE THE DAY

The future is just a stone's throw away! Use the mystic dictionary to decode the ancient runes to see what lies ahead...

TIME IN THE 3RD DIMENSION

Now, my magical apprentices, you can perform a truly bamboozling and brilliant spell to look into the future!

① Place the design you want to use face down on the surface you are working on. Fold the paper into quarters, crease well, and then unfold.

② Fold in each of the paper's corners, to meet in the middle.

③ Flip over the paper then repeat **step 1** on the new side.

④ Repeat **step 2**, folding in each corner to meet in the middle.

⑤ Fold and unfold into quarters, one last time.

⑥ Open out and slide your fingers into the pockets in the paper.

SHAZAMBLE!

HOW TO USE YOUR FORTUNE TELLER

1. Choose one of the words on the outer four squares. Spell out the word, alternating opening the fortune teller. In other words: open once for each letter first forwards, then to the sides.

2. When you've finished spelling the word, choose a number from the four inner squares on display. Count to the number, again alternating opening the fortune teller.

3. Choose one more number, and open the corresponding flap to reveal your fortune!

FANTASTICAL FUTURES

What does the future hold? Discover what's in store for you!

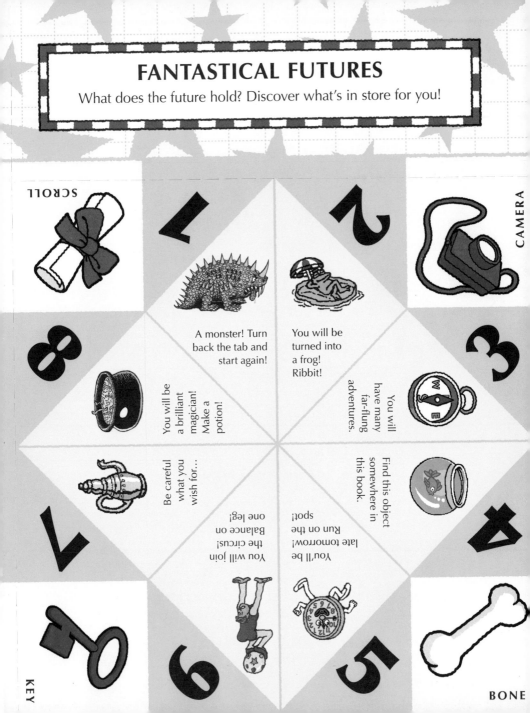

SCROLL

1

2

CAMERA

8

A monster! Turn back the tab and start again!

You will be turned into a frog! Ribbit!

3

You will be a brilliant magician! Make a potion!

You will have many far-flung adventures.

Be careful what you wish for…

Find this object somewhere in this book.

You will join the circus! Balance on one leg!

You'll be late tomorrow! Run on the spot!

7

6

5

4

KEY

BONE

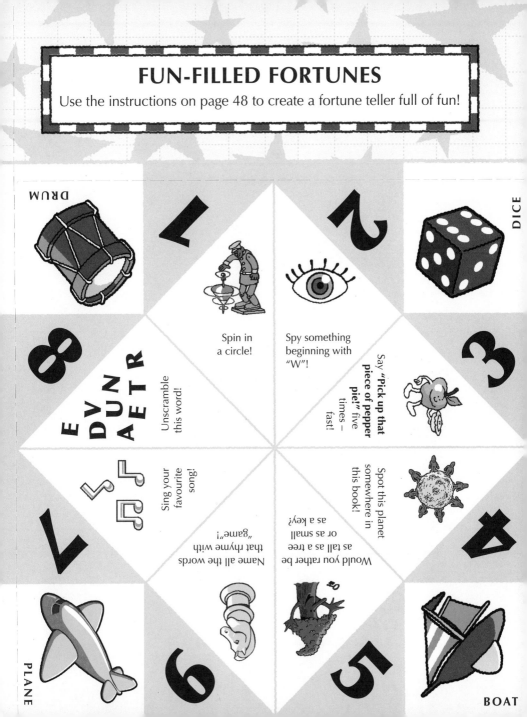

DRUM

DICE

PLANE

BOAT

1

2

3

4

5

6

7

8

Spin in a circle!

Spy something beginning with "W"!

Say **"Pick up that piece of pepper pie!"** five times – fast!

Unscramble this word!

E D V N U A E T R

Sing your favourite song!

Spot this planet somewhere in this book!

Name all the words that rhyme with "game"!

Would you rather be as tall as a tree or as small as a key?

FUNNY FORTUNES
Use the instructions on page 48 to create a rib-tickling fortune teller!

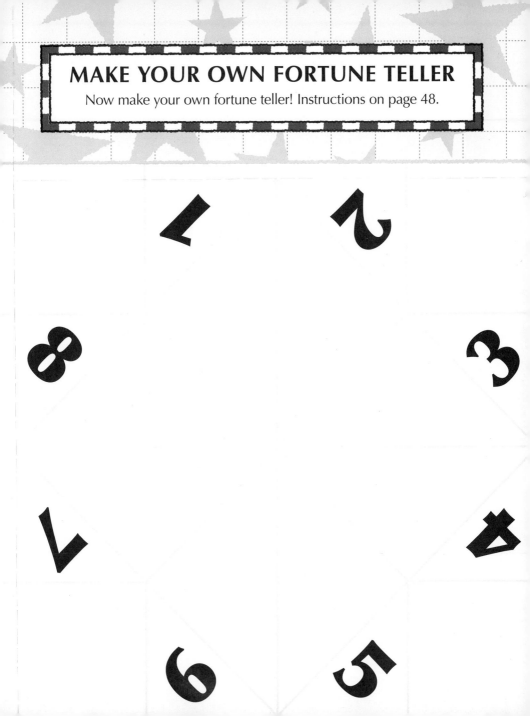

MAKE YOUR OWN FORTUNE TELLER

Now make your own fortune teller! Instructions on page 48.

VICIOUS VAMPIRE

Use the the fortune teller instructions on page 48 to create a creature of the night!

GRUESOME GROWLER

Use the instructions on page 48 to create a
menacing monster, but be careful … it might bite!

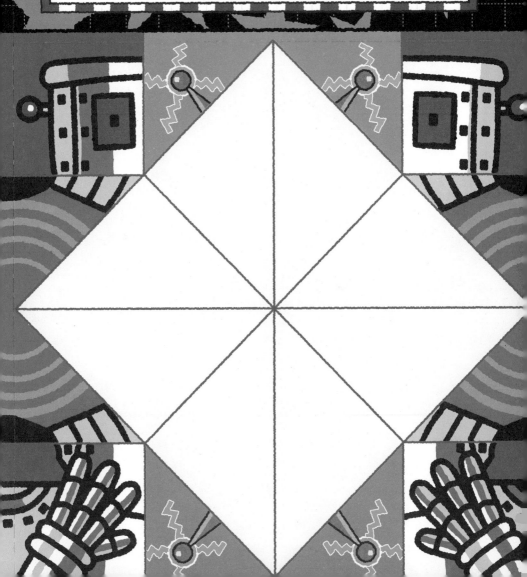

ROBOT GONE ROGUE

Use the instructions on page 48
to programme your robot!

MAKE YOUR OWN MINI MONSTER

Now make your monster a fierce friend! Doodle your
design below then use the instructions on page 48.

SILLY SCRIPT!

Puppeteer a conversation between your monstrous creations!
Fill in the list below, choosing different words for each line
(unless it says "Same") then turn the page.

1. Greeting *HELLO* ....

2. Name: .... **WARTY GRETEL** ....

3. Greeting: ....

4. Name: ....

5. Location: ....

6. Adjective: ....

7. Creature: ....

8. Name: ....

9. Adjective: ....

10. Adjective: ....

11. Food item: ....

12. Same food item: ....

13. Body part: ....

14. Colour: ....

15. Adjective: ....

16. Same adjective: ....

17. Verb: ....

SILLY SCRIPT CONTINUED!

Add your words from the previous page
in order, then act out the chat!

Monster A: 1 .....GOOD MORNING..,

2 .....WARTY GRETEL............... how have you been?

Monster B: 3 .... , 4 ....

I just came back from 5 ....!

I met a 6 .... 7 .... called

8 ....

Monster A: That sounds 9 .... !

Are you hungry? I have 10 ....

11 .... here.

Monster B: No thanks, 12 ....

makes my 13 ....

turn 14 .... !

Monster A: That's 15 .... !

Monster B: You're 16 .... !

Monster A: Let's go 17 ....!

MORE THINGS TO DO

* Create a whole new conversation by having your friends and family add their own words, using the list on page 65 as a guide.

FRAZZLED FIGHT

What a fierce fright night fight! But something's amiss. Can you spot ten differences between these two scenes?

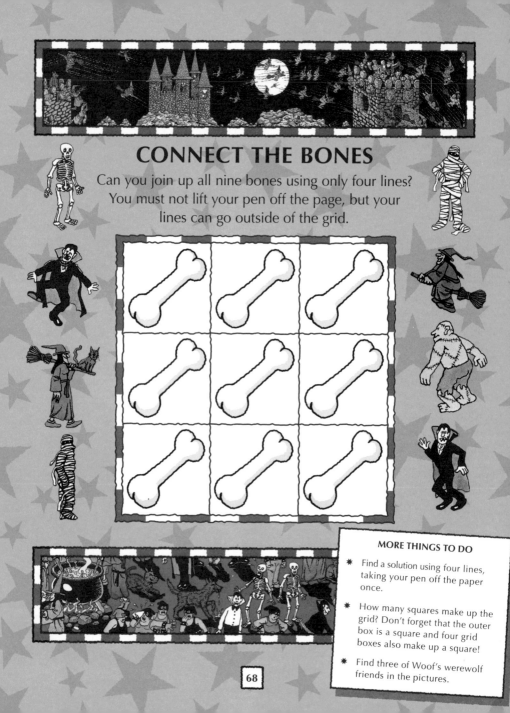

CONNECT THE BONES

Can you join up all nine bones using only four lines?
You must not lift your pen off the page, but your
lines can go outside of the grid.

MORE THINGS TO DO

* Find a solution using four lines, taking your pen off the paper once.

* How many squares make up the grid? Don't forget that the outer box is a square and four grid boxes also make up a square!

* Find three of Woof's werewolf friends in the pictures.

FRANKENSTEIN'S LABORATORY

Oh no, a mad scientist has mixed up these poor characters! Can you match the top half of each creation to their original bottom half?

MORE THINGS TO FIND

- [ ] A carrot
- [ ] A telescope
- [ ] Starry paint
- [ ] A vulture
- [ ] A green-and-white striped tie

70

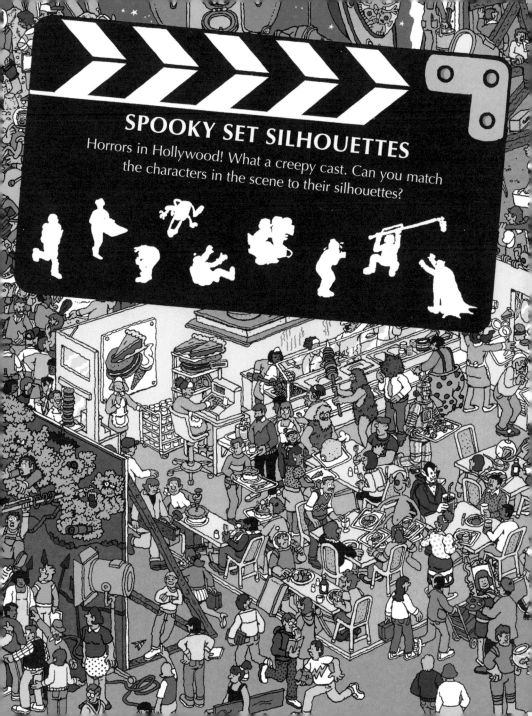

SPOOKY SET SILHOUETTES

Horrors in Hollywood! What a creepy cast. Can you match the characters in the scene to their silhouettes?

WHICH SCRIPT?

Each of these scenes is taken from a big picture, but which one is which? Match the synopsis to the screen shot!

SCENE 1: Helicopter Hélio almost makes his escape ... but then he hears the terrible whoosh of the rocket.

SCENE 2: Victor the vampire was just waking up for the night.

SCENE 3: The eccentric Lady Rowena likes to make a grand entrance!

SCENE 4: Helga is as pretty as a picture ... literally! Whose fairy tale kiss will free her?

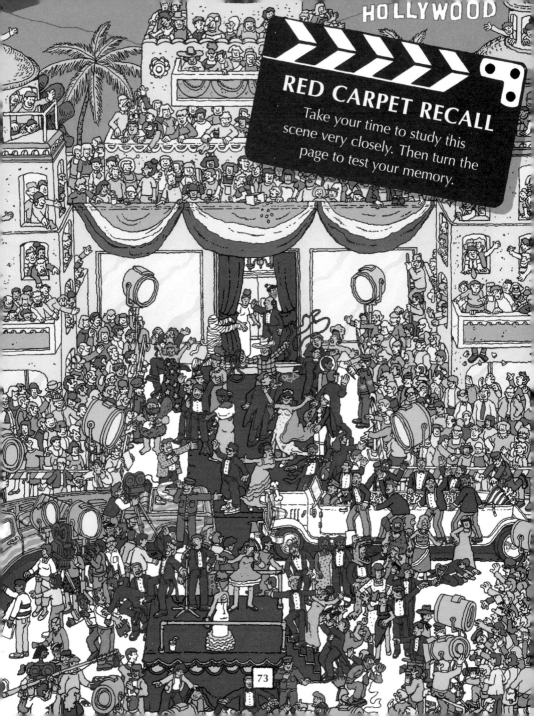

HOLLYWOOD

RED CARPET RECALL

Take your time to study this scene very closely. Then turn the page to test your memory.

Here we go! See how many of these questions you can answer from memory (It's also fun to guess!). Then turn back the page to see how you did.

What colour is the starry stretch limo?

☐ Blue
☐ Yellow
☐ Pink

How many spotlights are there?

☐ Eleven
☐ Seventeen
☐ Fourteen

Which ghoulish A-lister is coming down the red carpet?

☐ A mummy
☐ A vampire
☐ A ghost

Which way is the traffic controller directing cars?

☐ Right
☐ Left
☐ Both

Which creature costume features amongst the movie stars?

☐ A crocodile suit
☐ A gorilla suit
☐ A lion suit

What is Woof's car full of?

☐ Cats
☐ Chew toys
☐ Bones

EXTRA STAR-STRUCK SEARCHES

Study these close-ups carefully then turn back the page to find them!

REEL-ING

Look closely at each of these film reels. Wally appears in each one of these scenes except one – can you work out which?

THE WRITERS' ROOM

Write your own movies! Fill in the clapper boards and plan your plot in the space below.

THINGS TO THINK ABOUT

* Who will be in your movie?
* Will there be any twists or turns?
* Will it be funny? Scary? Exciting?
* Will the characters live happily ever after?

TITLE:

TAG LINE:

STARRING:

STORY:

TITLE:

TAG LINE:

STARRING:

STORY:

BRILLIANT BILLBOARD

Now that you've written your plot, it's time to promote your movie! Draw a poster on this billboard.

A BREAK-OUT ROLE

Sneak out of this silent movie! Follow this lamp-shaded lead to make a break for it:

❶ **Find** your star (clue: he's standing in front of a wardrobe).

❷ **Side-step** through the butterfly catchers and climb the ladder, sneaking past the man in the boater hat.

❸ **Climb** onto the elephant's back and slide down its trunk (watch out for the buckets of water!)

❹ **Hop** onto the trampoline and bounce past the firefighters over the wall.

❺ **Slide** past the bystanders and quickly cross the road, avoiding the motorbike and sidecar.

❻ **Crouch** down to avoid the smoke and crawl past the dog walkers ...

❼ ... and onto the train! Full steam ahead!

MAKE A BRILLIANT BOOKMARK!

Here's how to make a brilliant bookmark to keep track of all the pandemonium between these pages!

1 Start with the paper in a diamond shape, the image side facing down, with the character face at the top.

2 Fold the paper in half diagonally to make a triangle.

3 Fold the top point of your triangle down to meet the base at point "A".

4 Fold both bottom corners in to meet in the middle at point "A".

5 Fold the bottom two corners in to meet the triangle's point at "B", then crease.

6 Turn over the paper. Ta-da! Slide your new bookmark onto the corner of this book!

WALLY BOOKMARK

For amazing adventures! Follow the instructions on page 80.

Start
folding
with this side of
the paper upwards.
This message should be at
the top corner of the paper.

ODLAW BOOKMARK

For terrible tales! Follow the instructions on page 80.

Start
folding
with this side of
the paper upwards.
This message should be at
the top corner of the paper.

WOOF FINGER PUPPET

Follow the instructions on page 89 for a puppet pooch. Make your puppet's ears floppy like Woof's by folding down the tips!

Fold over
Woof's ear here

Fold over
Woof's ear here

MAKE YOUR OWN FINGER PUPPET

Use the instructions on page 89 to create your puppet. You can add extra accessories and colour for even more fun!

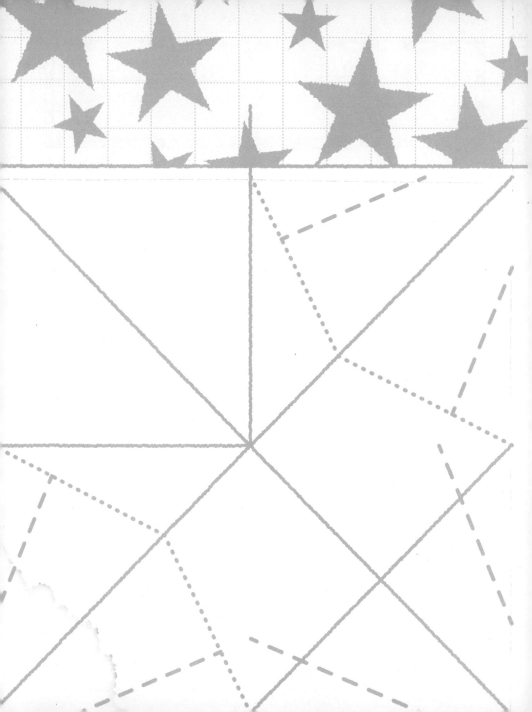

THEATRICAL FINGER PUPPET

Time for your paper-folding skills to once again take centre stage. Here's how to make magnificent finger puppets!

1 Start with the paper arranged in a diamond shape, with the face at the top.

2 Fold the paper into a triangle vertically, and then unfold it.

3 Next, fold the paper down horizontally.

4 Fold left and right corners of the triangle down to the bottom point, to make a diamond.

5 Fold the top layer of the diamond back along the dotted line so that each side goes beyond the edge of the paper.

6 Fold back the top layer of the bottom of the paper to meet the top point.

7 Turn the paper over and fold the left and right-hand sides in to meet the lines on the template.

8 Fold the bottom point up to meet the top point.

9 Turn the model over and fold all layers of the top point over and tuck behind.

Slide your finger into the pocket at the bottom of the paper. Ta-da! Your very own finger puppet friend!

THE SUPER SEARCH CUBE!

Use the square paper from the front and back of this book to make TWO amazing 3D search cubes! Follow the instructions below, then turn to page 92 for some super searches!

FOLDING YOUR CUBE

TOP TIP: Match the coloured shapes on the template as you fold!

1 Take six sheets of paper with a matching blue symbol. Start with one piece of paper, scene-side down on the surface you are working on.

2 Fold the two sides into the centre of the paper, using the dotted lines as a guide.

3 Fold in both the top and bottom of the paper along the dotted lines to meet in the centre and crease well.

4 Undo the fold from **step 3** so that both ends of the paper stand upright.

5 Repeat **steps 2 to 4** with the other five pieces of paper.

Now you are ready to assemble your cube!

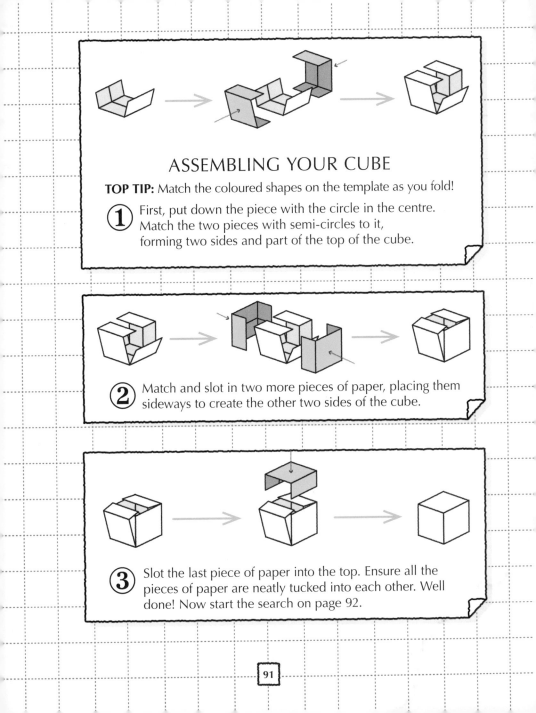

ASSEMBLING YOUR CUBE

TOP TIP: Match the coloured shapes on the template as you fold!

(1) First, put down the piece with the circle in the centre. Match the two pieces with semi-circles to it, forming two sides and part of the top of the cube.

(2) Match and slot in two more pieces of paper, placing them sideways to create the other two sides of the cube.

(3) Slot the last piece of paper into the top. Ensure all the pieces of paper are neatly tucked into each other. Well done! Now start the search on page 92.

CRAZY CUBE CHECKLIST 1:
SPACE-TACULAR SEARCH CUBE!

Search all six sides of your space-tastic cube to find the items below.

CHECKLIST

- [ ] Mercury
- [ ] The Milky Way
- [ ] A red monster with yellow tentacles
- [ ] Two flying teacups
- [ ] Eight red aliens
- [ ] A trident
- [ ] Hitchhikers
- [ ] An amber traffic light
- [ ] The Great Bear
- [ ] A spanner
- [ ] Thirteen yellow stars
- [ ] Seven astronauts in orange spacesuits
- [ ] Two crashed rockets
- [ ] Three ringed planets
- [ ] Seven astronauts in blue spacesuits
- [ ] A planet with a smiley face
- [ ] A space shuttle bus
- [ ] A red flying saucer
- [ ] Two dogs on space walks
- [ ] Two rockets with green stripes
- [ ] Five astronauts in green spacesuits
- [ ] Five waving aliens
- [ ] Three yellow space vehicles
- [ ] A blue alien

Don't forget to look for Wally, too!

CRAZY CUBE CHECKLIST 2:
THREE WALLY WORLDS

THE GLORIOUS GARDEN

- [ ] A wilting watering can
- [ ] A tree house
- [ ] Patched-up cabbages
- [ ] Someone sticking out their tongue

THE PIRATE CAVE

- [ ] A sore foot
- [ ] A lounging looter
- [ ] A yellow patch
- [ ] A pink bolster

CAKE FACTORY CHAOS

- [ ] An egg-juggler
- [ ] An unhappy baker
- [ ] Someone slipping
- [ ] Two tiny bakers

Once you've found everything on the checklist, it's time to spot the difference! Can you find five differences between each corresponding scene *and* find Wally, the gang and their lost things?

CUBE-ISM

Why not play an extra game with your cube? Drop an object into it and challenge a friend to guess what's inside. They can ask up to twenty questions, and you can only reply "yes" or "no"!

ANSWERS

P 4 FLIGHT SCHOOL

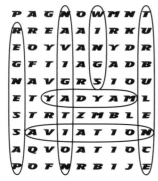

P 5 BAGGAGE CLAIM

The correct bag is this one:

P 6–7 RUNAWAY RUNWAY

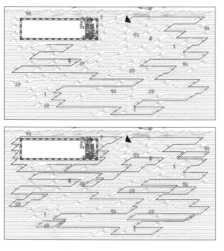

P 8 DESTINATION EVERYWHERE

Wally went from New York to São Paulo to
Rome to Tokyo.
Wenda went from London to Sydney.
Woof went from Hong Kong to Paris.
Wizard Whitebeard went from Amsterdam
but missed his flight at Toronto.
Odlaw went from Oslo but missed his
flight at Dubai.

P 9 WHERE TO?

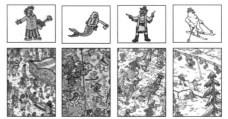

P 10-11 BIRDS OF A FEATHER

This is the odd one out:

P 36 TIME AND SPACE MAZE

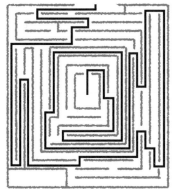

P 37 PLANETS ALIGNING

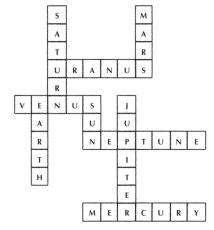

P 39 WANDERING LINES

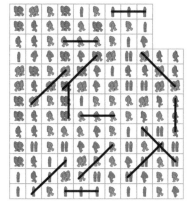

P 41 WRITTEN IN THE STARS

THERE IS MAGIC WITHIN YOU! SAY THIS STARRY SPELL: GREAT STARRY POWER, I SUMMON THEE. WITH AN ABRACADABRA ONE, TWO, THREE!

P 43 SPELL-DUKO

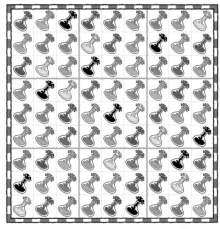

P 46 SPELL-TACULAR

Magic makes much mayhem

P 47 RUNE THE DAY

THE FUTURE IS BRIGHT! FIND A UNICORN
HIDING IN THIS BOOK.

P 68 CONNECT THE BONES

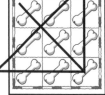

P 69 FRANKENSTEIN'S LABORATORY

P 72 WHICH SCRIPT?

SCENE 1   SCENE 2   SCENE 3

SCENE 4

First published 2020 by Walker Books Ltd, 87 Vauxhall Walk, London SE11 5HJ

2 4 6 8 10 9 7 5 3 1 © 1987–2020 Martin Handford. Use of the Hollywood sign™/©1993 Hollywood Chamber of Commerce under license authorized by Curtis Management Group, Indianapolis, Indiana, USA

The right of Martin Handford to be identified as author/illustrator of this work has been asserted by him in accordance with the Copyright, Designs and Patents Act 1988.

This book has been typeset in Wallyfont and Optima

Printed in China

British Library Cataloguing in Publication Data:
a catalogue record for this book is available
from the British Library.

ISBN 978-1-4063-9104-6

www.walker.co.uk

ONE FINAL, FINAL, THING ... YOU'VE SEARCHED THROUGH STARRY SPELL BOOKS AND MOVIE MAGIC, BUT DID YOU SPOT THE RABBIT? GO BACK AND FIND IT SOMEWHERE IN THIS BOOK! HINT: IT ISN'T IN A HAT!